Amazing Amelia

Susannah McFarlane   Lachlan Creagh

A Scholastic Australia Book

This is Amelia, with some of her friends—
Amy, Andy, Annie and Aaron.

Amelia is the most active and athletic ant on the anthill, actually in all Australia. She adores all activities and has awesome abilities!

She is an astonishing acrobat.

She is an amazing tennis ace.

And she is absolutely admired at Aussie Rules.

Then one day . . .

Aaaa

Amelia had an accident with her arms—oh how they ached!

Poor Amelia, it was awful!

She couldn't flip
in the air.

She couldn't ace
any animal.

And apparently, she
also wasn't able to
kick an AFL ball.

One afternoon, as she was eating an apple, Amelia had an amazing idea. She would be able to assist her friends with their athletic activities!

She assisted Aaron to bowl better.

She assisted Annie to hit harder.

She assisted Andy and Amy
to leap longer.

Amelia, you are an amazing,
A-plus friend agreed all her mates.

When Amelia was able, they all had the
most awesome athletics day ever.

At the end they all sang 'Australian ants let us rejoice'.

Good on you Amelia
(and Amy, Andy, Aaron
and Annie).

What about you?
Are you amazing too?